SIMPSONS COMICS
MELTDOWN

TITAN BOOKS

SIMPSONS COMICS MELTDOWN

Collects Simpsons Comics 91, 92, 93, 94, and 95

Copyright © 2004 & 2011 by
Bongo Entertainment, Inc. All rights reserved.
No part of this book may be used or reproduced in any manner whatsoever
without written permission except in the case of brief quotations
embodied in critical articles and reviews. For information address
Bongo Comics Group c/o Titan Books
P.O. Box 1963, Santa Monica, CA 90406-1963

Published in the UK by Titan Books, a division of Titan Publishing Group Ltd.,
144 Southwark St., London SE1 0UP, under licence from Bongo Entertainment, Inc.

FIRST EDITION: FEBRUARY 2011

ISBN 9780857681560

2 4 6 8 10 9 7 5 3 1

Publisher: Matt Groening
Creative Director: Bill Morrison
Managing Editor: Terry Delegeane
Director of Operations: Robert Zaugh
Art Director: Nathan Kane
Art Director Special Projects: Serban Cristescu
Production Manager: Christopher Ungar
Assistant Art Director: Chia-Hsien Jason Ho
Production/Design: Karen Bates, Nathan Hamill, Art Villanueva
Staff Artist: Mike Rote
Administration: Ruth Waytz, Pete Benson
Intern: Max Davison
Legal Guardian: Susan A. Grode

Trade Paperback Concepts and Design: Serban Cristescu

Contributing Artists:
Karen Bates, John Costanza, Serban Cristescu, Mike DeCarlo, Luis Escobar, Kevin M. Newman,
Phil Ortiz, Patrick Owsley, Howard Shum, and Art Villanueva

Contributing Writers:
Ian Boothby and Chuck Dixon

Printed by Quad/Graphics, Inc., Montreal, QC, Canada. 01/07/11

SIMPSONS COMICS
Meltdown

CONTENTS

100% FISSION FRESH!

:YAWN!:

FIRST DIBS ON THE BATHROOM!

WHAT?

WAIT! I LEFT MY TEETH WHITENING STRIPS IN TOO LONG!

I NEED TO BRUSH THEM OFF MY TEETH BEFORE THEY BLEACH THE REST OF MY HEAD!

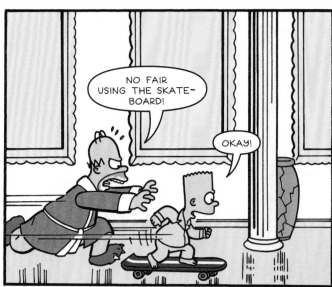

NO FAIR USING THE SKATE-BOARD!

OKAY!

YAAAAAAH!

:HEH, HEH!:

SHWIP!

HELLO, DEAR!

MORNING, DAD!

BACK O' THE LINE, HOMER!

:MOAN!:

ONE WEEK EARLIER...

"*COMING THIS FALL!* THEY'RE FOUR *SEXY* WOMEN OUT TO MARRY SPRINGFIELD'S *MOST ELIGIBLE BACHELOR!*"

"BUT HE'S GOT A *SECRET!*"

THANKS, BUT I'M JUST NOT INTERESTED!

IT'S NOT *YOU*, IT'S *ME!*

"*JOE SURPRISE!* THURSDAYS AT NINE!"

EWW...

CUT! I SAY, WELL DONE EVERY-ONE!

MR. BURNS, I JUST DON'T FEEL COMFORTABLE WITH THIS.

PISH TOSH! THIS *DECLAN DESMOND* FELLOW HAS AGREED TO FILM THE PROGRAM HERE AT THE NUCLEAR PLANT.

WE NEED SOME TELEVISION COVERAGE THAT *ISN'T* A "60 MINUTES" EXPOSÉ!

WHAT? *MIKE WALLACE?!* YOU'RE STILL *EMBEDDED* HERE?

YES! NOW EITHER COME CLEAN ABOUT YOUR CRIMES AGAINST THE ENVIRONMENT OR FLUFF MY PILLOW!

BAD NEWS, CHAPS. THE NET-WORK HAS CUT OUR SHOW FROM THE FALL LINE-UP.

≡WHEW!≡

WHAT? WHY?

FLUFF!

THE DATING SHOW THING HAS BEEN DONE TO DEATH. ALL PEOPLE WANT NOW ARE "JACKASS"-STYLE STUNTS DONE BY REAL-LIFE IDIOTS.

IT'S BACK TO ENGLAND FOR ME. I WONDER IF BBC'S "ROYAL FAMILY BLOOPERS AND PRACTICAL JOKES" IS STILL HIRING.

OOOH! RIGHT IN THE CROWN JEWELS!

THWACK!

:SHUDDER!:

WAIT! WE HAVE PLENTY OF IDIOTS HERE!

SSSSSSS!

GAAAAAH!

BLIMEY!

THUD!

SORRY, MR. BURNS. LENNY ASKED ME TO GET RID OF THIS NUCLEAR WASTE, BUT I SPILLED SOME ON THE FLOOR LIKE THIS AND...

SSSSSSSS!

I LOVE HIM!

GAAAAAH!

I FIND YOU, C. MONTGOMERY BURNS, *GUILTY* OF RELEASING A RADIOACTIVE CLOUD OVER SPRINGFIELD AND MAKING THE TOWN *UNINHABITABLE!*

INCLUDING MY *COURTHOUSE!*

YES, YES, JUST GET ON WITH THE SENTENCE. MY CHEF NEEDS HIS MEAT TENDERIZER BACK!

"YOUR MANSION IS THE ONLY BUILDING THAT'S STILL ABOVE THE RADIOACTIVE CLOUD. UNTIL IT IS SAFE FOR THEM TO RETURN HOME, *YOU MUST HOUSE THE ENTIRE TOWN OF SPRINGFIELD!*"

WIPE YOUR FEET!

DON'T TOUCH ANYTHING!

NO GOATS!

MONTY, THIS IS THE BREAK WE NEED. I'LL MAKE A SHOW OUT OF *THIS*. A WHOLE TOWN UNDER ONE ROOF! IT'S NEVER BEEN DONE BEFORE!

AND EVERY DAY WE *ELIMINATE* ONE OF THEM.

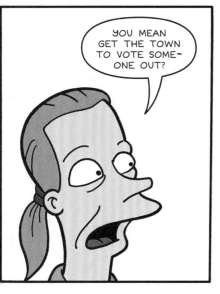

YOU MEAN GET THE TOWN TO VOTE SOME- ONE OUT?

I *MEANT* HUNT THEM FOR SPORT.

BUT WE'LL PLAY IT YOUR WAY.

FOR NOW.

AND SO...

IT'S MORNING IN THE MANSION THAT I'VE VERY CLEVERLY DUBBED THE "TOWN" HOUSE! LET'S LOOK IN ON A TYPICAL FAMILY.

GAME ROOM

BART! GET UP! DON'T MAKE ME TILT YOU!

RADIOACTIVE MAN

⌇MOAN!⌇ JUST LET ME SLEEP TWO MORE GAMES!

RADIOACTIVE MAN

MOM, I THINK MAGGIE'S STUCK!

SUCK! SUCK!

⌇GROAN!⌇ MARGE? LITTLE HELP POPPING MY SPINE BACK INTO PLACE?

THIS **BLOWS**. I MISS OUR HOME!

WE JUST HAVE TO MAKE DO FOR NOW. GRIN AND BEAR IT! NOW EAT YOUR BREAKFAST.

MARGE, PASS THE SAUSAGE?

YOU **GOT** IT!

SPINNN!

SWACK!

GOOOOOOOAL!

:GULP!:

AND WHAT ROOM OF THE MANSION ARE *YOU* IN AGAIN, COMIC BOOK GUY?

NOT A ROOM AT ALL. USING CITY BLUEPRINTS I DOWNLOADED FROM THE INTERNET, I DISCOVERED A *SECRET CAVE* UNDERNEATH THE MANSION.

I HAVE RENOVATED IT TO BE MY SECRET SANCTUARY, JUST LIKE *BATMAN!*

STAR WARS

BUCKAROO BANZAI

SCHOOL

IT LOOKS LIKE YOUR PARENT'S BASEMENT. HOW IS *THIS* LIKE BATMAN?

BATMAN LIVES IN *HIS* PARENT'S BASEMENT!

SPECTACULAR SPIDER-MAN

PETER PARKER THE SPECTACULAR SPIDER-MAN

AUNT MAY'S SPECTACULAR SEXY SPRING BREAK ADVENTURES

PETER PARKER: SPECTACULAR SPIDER-MAN

HELLO, GENTLE VIEWERS IN TV LAND! I AM PROFESSOR JOHN FRINK, CURRENTLY RESIDING IN MR. BURNS' HUNTING TROPHY ROOM ≡GA-HAVEN≡.

IT'S IMPRESSIVE!

EVEN MORE SO NOW THAT I'VE INSERTED MY OWN ANIMATRONIC SKELETONS THAT I CONTROL WITH THIS REMOTE.

JUST A FEW SIMPLE TURNS OF THE KNOBS AND...

WRRRRRRRR!

OH SWEET GLAVIN!

FZZT!

IT'S...

MONTY'S PYTHON!

RUN FOR YOUR LIVES!

KENT'S PEOPLE

LATER THAT NIGHT...

OH FOR CRYING OUT LOUD! IT'S BAD ENOUGH THAT THERE'S NO HEAT AND I HAVE TO SLEEP WITH MEL FOR WARMTH WITH HIS BONE POKING ME ALL NIGHT!

THAT *IS* YOUR *BONE*, RIGHT?

FOR THE LAST TIME, *YES!*

BUT THIS IS TOO MUCH! KEEP IT DOWN!

YEAH, KNOCK IT OFF!

BANG!

BANG!

NO CAN DO! I GOT THE MUSIC IN MY SOUL AND A BATTERY-POWERED AMP!

WE DIDN'T WANT TO DO THIS, BUT YOU'VE LEFT US NO CHOICE.

THIS IS HIGHLY INSULTING TO BOTH ME *AND* THE WORLD OF JAZZ.

IT'S NOT WORKING! WE HAVE NO CHOICE BUT TO USE *EXTREME MEASURES!*

CHIEF, YOU DON'T MEAN...

RELEASE THE *SCOTSMAN!*

CLICK!

SWEET MERCIFUL GLAVIN!

HONK!

BLEAT!

BLAT!

HONK!

I SURRENDER! I SURRENDER!

WE WON, CHIEF!

⊱SIGH⊰ WHEN IT GOES THIS FAR, LOU, *NOBODY* WINS.

WHICH BRINGS US BACK TO THE PRESENT...

THERE'S NO MORE WATER! THE PLUMBING'S DRIER THAN A STEVEN WRIGHT MONOLOGUE!

WE'LL DIE OF THIRST!

NO WE *WON'T!*

THERE'S STILL THE POOL WATER!

FORGOT ABOUT THE BARRACUDAS, HUH, DAD?

YEAH, YEAH...

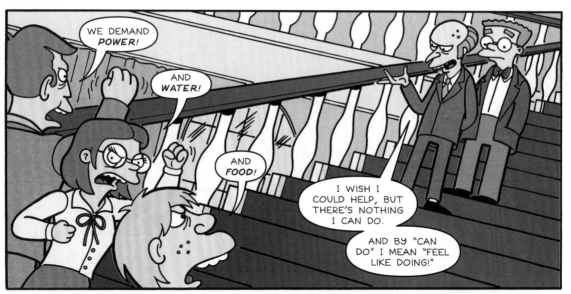

THEN GO TO PLAN B!

THERE *ISN'T* ONE. WE HAD TO CUT BACK EXPENSES ON ALL YOUR PLANS TO JUST *A'S* WHEN YOUR DOT COM COMPANY FOLDED, SIR.

ONLY ONE HIT AGAIN TODAY AT SEXYMONTYPICS.ORG. I DON'T KNOW HOW YOU CONVINCED ME TO SET THIS SITE UP, SMITHERS.

I'M SURE THAT ONE SURFER IS VERY LOYAL, SIR.

YAAAAAAAA!

WAIT! WAIT! *THIS* AIN'T RIGHT!

WHAT DO YOU MEAN, MOE?

IT AIN'T A *REAL* ANGRY MOB WITHOUT PITCHFORKS AND TORCHES!

THERE YA GO! NO SHOVING! WE GOT LOTS!

ACME ANGRY MOB TORCHES *and* PITCHFORKS

THEY'VE SEEN THROUGH MY BRILLIANT DISGUISE!

PERHAPS A BRIBE!

HERE, WHY ATTACK WHEN I'LL LET YOU EAT CAKE!

MMMMM!

YUM!

HEH, HEH! HE WAS RIGHT, THAT CAKE WAS JUST THE PRESCRIPTION WE NEEDED!

YOU KNOW, I WAS TOO WEAK TO *REALLY* STORM THE MANSION, BUT THAT CAKE HAS GIVEN ME THE *QUICK ENERGY* I NEED!

LET'S *GET* HIM!

CURSE YOU, BETTY CROCKER! THE OLD GYPSY *SAID* YOU'D BE MY DOWNFALL!

SO THE WORST IT COULD DO IS MOISTEN YOUR SKIN?

NOT THAT *YOU'D* NEED IT, BEAUTIFUL!

SEYMOUR, IT'S *ME*!

MOTHER! AHHHH!

BUT *WHO*? WHO COULD BE RESPONSIBLE FOR THE RUSE? WHO HAD THE MEANS AND MOTIVATION?

IT'S A FAIR COP!

I WANTED A HIT SHOW, AND SO I *FAKED* THE ACCIDENT SO YOU'D ALL HAVE TO LIVE TOGETHER.

YOU WANNA RUSH HIM?

I'M TOO TIRED. BEING PART OF AN ANGRY MOB REALLY TAKES IT OUT OF YOU.

AND SO...

LET'S GO HOME.

NOT SO FAST!

YOU ALMOST GOT ME KILLED AND MY HOME BURNED TO THE GROUND!

YOUR PLAN WAS SO DEVIOUS, SO CRUEL AND SELFISH...

...THAT I JUST CAN'T STAY MAD AT YOU.

WELL, IF YOU'RE NOT GOING TO KILL ME, I DO HAVE *ANOTHER* SHOW IDEA I WANT TO RUN BY YOU.

Springfield Idol

♪ ...THAT IN THE SPRING...BECOMES ...THE ROSE! ♪

THAT WAS THE *BOMB*, DOG!

I LOVE IT. I FELT IT. IT *MOVED* ME!

THE LAST NOTE WAS A G-FLAT. IT SHOULD HAVE BEEN A G-*SHARP!*

RELEASE THE HOUNDS!

I SMELL A HIT!

AND THE SPCA DOESN'T MIND YOU USING THE HOUNDS?

NO, THE ONLY *CRUELTY* IS TO THE *CONTESTANTS.*

GROWL!

BARK!

SNARL!

MONITOR 4

MONITOR

MONITOR

GENTLEMEN, A TOAST...TO THE *EVILS* OF REALITY TV!

AAAAH!

NOW *THERE'S* THAT G-SHARP!

CLINK!

THE END

THE BURGER KINGS OF COMEDY!

A MATT GROENING PRODUCTION

CHUCK **DIXON** SCRIPT JOHN **COSTANZA** PENCILS HOWARD **SHUM** INKS ART **VILLANUEVA** COLORS KAREN **BATES** LETTERS BILL **MORRISON** EDITOR

WAFFLE-APOGUS! BREAKFAST WILL NEVER BE THE SAME!

PANCAKES ARE FOR SISSIES! GIMME A WAFFLE-APOGUS!

LIMITED TIME ONLY!

WAFFLE-APOGUS!

IT'S THE *GREATEST* BREAKFAST TREAT SINCE PIZZA POCKET BREAKFAST BURRITO MUFFINS!

MMM... WAFFLES.

I JUST *GAVE* YOU WAFFLES, HOMER. THEY'RE RIGHT IN *FRONT* OF YOU.

BUT WAFFLE-APOGUS IS *DIFFERENT*, MARGE. IT'S KEPT *TOASTY* IN A STYROFOAM SHELL AND HAS THOSE LITTLE PLASTIC PACKETS OF *SYRUP*!

IT'S A *LUMBERJACK* BREAKFAST! NOT LIKE THESE FOO-FOO *BELGIAN* WAFFLE WANNABES!

BREAKFAST WILL NEVER BE THE *SAME*, MARGE!

NEVER.

BE.

THE.

SAME!

AND THERE'S A "BUY ONE GET ONE FREE" COUPON.

BUY ONE GET ONE FREE!

GOTTA *GO!* MARGE, WHERE'S MY *TIE?*

YOU DON'T *WEAR* A TIE.

I'LL BE LATE FOR *WORK!*

YOU'RE *ALWAYS* LATE FOR WORK.

NO TIME TO *ARGUE*, WOMAN!

CALL LENNY AND CARL AND TELL THEM TO BE WAITING OUT *FRONT!*

WHAM!

D'OH!

OOF!

I'M SORRY. MY HUSBAND'S EXCITED ABOUT A NEW ITEM DOWN AT *KRUSTY-BURGER.*

WHAT'S *WITH* THE PEOPLE ON THIS ROUTE? I GOT *ANOTHER* GUY OBSESSED WITH *SANDWICHES* TWO BLOCKS OVER.

WAFFLE-WAFFLE-WAFFLE!

ARE YOU HURT?

I'D *SAY* ONLY MY PRIDE...

...BUT I'M A *MAIL-MAN.*

A MAILMAN WITH A GARAGE FULL OF AMMO.

WHAT *IS* IT WITH DAD AND THESE FAST FOOD PROMOTIONS?

I HOPE HE DOESN'T GO ON *TOUR* LIKE HE DID WITH THE RIBWICH.

NO *SWEAT,* MOM. THIS IS A *NATIONAL* ROLL-OUT.

THANK GOODNESS FOR SMALL FAVORS. *RIGHT,* MAGGIE?

I HOPE *YOU* DON'T GROW UP AND FALL FOR EVERY SALES PITCH YOU SEE.

NOW, YOU WATCH SOME COMMERCIAL-*FREE* CHILDREN'S PROGRAMMING ON PBS WHILE MOMMY STRAIGHTENS THE KITCHEN.

WE TAKE A SHORT BREAK FROM *"BOOKBUG AND THE ALPHA-BEES"*--

--TO REMIND YOU KIDS THAT FOR A MERE $250 PLEDGE THIS READ-2-ME BOOKBUG CAN BE *YOURS!*

TELL YOUR PARENTS TO GET ON THE HORN, OR YOU'LL NEVER SEE BOOKBUG *AGAIN!*

ACROSS TOWN...

I'LL KILL YOU!

I'LL KILL YOU!

KER-ACK!

I'M *SORRY*, SIR! BUT THIS COUPON IS ONLY GOOD UNTIL NINE O'CLOCK.

POW!

TOUGH *LUCK*, HOMER.

C'MON, WE CAN GET WAFFLES AT *PANCAKE PALACE*.

NO!

I HAVE A *COUPON*, AND I'M *USING* IT! I DON'T CARE *HOW* LONG I HAVE TO WAIT!

SIR, YOU *HAVE* TO CALM DOWN.

THE *POLICE* ARE HERE.

IT *NEVER* FAILS. I *ALWAYS* PULL IN BEHIND SOMEONE WITH A BIG ORDER.

SAME THING WITH *ME* AT THE BANK.

GRRRR!

AS GOD IS MY *WITNESS*...

...I'LL NEVER GO HUNGRY FOR *WAFFLES* AGAIN!

CASHIER

I'M *THROUGH* BEING PUSHED AROUND! YOU *HEAR* ME?

YEAH, BUT WHAT CAN THE LITTLE MAN *DO?*

CARL'S *RIGHT*. IT'S NOT LIKE YOU CAN *CHANGE* ANYTHING.

OH *YEAH?*

SOMETIMES ALL IT TAKES IS *ONE* MAN TO MAKE A DIFFERENCE...LIKE IN THAT *MOVIE* WHERE ONE MAN MAKES A DIFFERENCE.

I'LL BEAT THAT CLOWN AT HIS OWN *GAME...*

SOON...

YOU WANT TO BUY A *FRANCHISE*, MR SIMPSON?

DARN *TOOTIN'.*

KRUSTYCO INTERNATIONAL

I SEE YOU'VE MORTGAGED YOUR HOUSE...

...FOR THE *SIXTEENTH* TIME.

AND CASHED IN YOUR *LIFE* INSURANCE AND YOUR CHILDREN'S *COLLEGE* FUND AND ANY FUTURE EARNINGS FROM THE TOOTH FAIRY.

THREE KIDS, STILL WITH *BABY TEETH*, SIR.

WELL, ALL *LOOKS* TO BE IN ORDER.

SO, I HAVE MY *OWN* KRUSTY-BURGER?

YOU NEED TO GO TO THE *KRUSTY KULINARY INSTITUTE* FIRST.

I NEED TO *LEARN* STUFF?

SURE. ALL ABOUT MEAT PATTIES AND FRENCH FRIES AND THE PROPER RATIO OF LARD TO CHOCOLATE IN A KRUSTYSHAKE AND...

GAAHHH... LARD...

AT SPRINGFIELD ELEMENTARY...

NOW WITH 20% MORE KID PER CLASS!

"WHAT DID *YOU* BRING FOR LUNCH, LISA?"

ORGANIC ALFALFA SPROUTS AND BEAN CURD HUMMUS ON A BULGAR WHEAT CROISSANT.

WHAT ARE *YOU* GUYS EATING?

A MR. TEENY BURGER.

A DELICIOUS CHOCOLATE KRUSTYSHAKE.

SIDESHOW FRIES.

HUH?

MCBAIN VII: LICENSE TO GRILL!

BUT WHERE DID YOU--?

OH NO!

OUR SCHOOL HAS BEEN *CO-OPTED* BY CORPORATE AMERICA!

KRUSTYCO EDU-KATERING LIMITED

KRUSTY SUPPORTS LEARNING!

MY BURGER TASTES *CRUNCHY*.

YOU BIT THE HEAD OFF OF YOUR MCBAIN ACTION FIGURE.

THAT AFTERNOON...

I DON'T SEE WHY YOU'RE SO *BUMMED*. EVERYONE *LOVES* KRUSTY-BURGER, LIS.

I DON'T EVEN WANT TO *THINK* ABOUT IT ANY-MORE.

AT LEAST WE'RE *HOME* WHERE I DON'T HAVE TO SMELL COOKED FLESH UNTIL *DINNERTIME* AND--

NO! IT CAN'T BE!

WHAT FRESH HELL IS *THIS*?

KIDS, YOUR *DAD* IS NOW THE OWNER OF SPRINGFIELD'S *NEWEST* KRUSTYBURGER FRANCHISE!

AND THEY RE-MODELED THE CAR FOR *FREE*!

WOW, HOMER!

YOU'RE THE COOLEST DAD IN THE *WORLD*!

ISN'T HOMER THE *COOLEST* DAD, MOM?

HRMMM...

YOUR MOTHER'S STILL DEALING WITH THE *SURPRISE*, BOY.

I *THOUGHT* I WAS ASHAMED OF YOUR JOB AT THE *NUCLEAR* PLANT...

...BUT *NOW* YOU'VE BECOME A WILLING TOOL OF THE *SATURATED FAT* CARTEL!

AW, WHY CAN'T YOU BE *HAPPY* LIKE EVERYONE ELSE, LISA?

YOU'LL BE *POISONING* AMERICA WITH YOUR EMPTY CALORIES AND ARTERY-CLOGGING TRANSFATS!

OBVIOUSLY YOU HAVEN'T TRIED OUR BACON AND MOZARELLA *SPROUT*BURGER.

DON'T *SPOIL* THIS, LISA! WE COULD BE THE MOST *POPULAR* KIDS IN SCHOOL!

WAY MORE POPULAR THAN THAT KID WHO DATED DEMI MOORE!

DON'T YOU *REALIZE* THAT THESE FAST FOOD TOXINS TAKE TWENTY YEARS OFF YOUR LIFE?

DID I LEAVE MY *TEETH* HERE?

A SHINY *QUARTER* FOR THE LUCKY FELLER THAT FINDS 'EM!

ACTUALLY? THE TRADE-OFF SEEMS *FAIR*, LIS.

I GIVE UP.

THE OSCAR MEYER *WIENERMOBILE!* CAN I HAVE A *WHISTLE?*

I'M GOING *INSIDE!* JUST *LOOKING* AT OUR CAR IS RAISING MY CHOLESTEROL!

THE NEXT DAY...

KRUSTY KULINARY INSTITUTE

"IT ALL BEGINS ON THE GRASSY PAMPAS OF PATAGONIA..."

WHAT IS IT *NOW*, MR. SIMPSON?

THIS MOVIE IS *STUPID!* THIS *MANUAL* IS STUPID!

AND I SUPPOSE YOU ALREADY *KNOW* ALL THIS?

YOU GOT *THAT* RIGHT.

I'VE BEEN A LOYAL KRUSTYBURGER CUSTOMER FOR *YEARS!* THERE'S NOTHING YOU CAN TEACH *ME.*

OKAY, SMARTYPANTS!

PROVE IT BY TAKING THIS STANDARDIZED TEST!

WHUMP!

MINUTES LATER...

...HM...MM... UM...

AN HOUR PASSES...

WELL?

THIS SCORE IS...*PERFECT!*

I'VE NEVER SEEN ANYTHING *LIKE* IT. YOU'RE *BORN* KRUSTY-BURGER MATERIAL, MR. SIMPSON.

WOO-HOO!

WHEN DO I GET MY *RESTAURANT?*

YOU CROOKED CLOWN!

I WAS PROMISED I'D BE THE **ONLY** KRUSTY-BURGER FOR ONE POINT THREE MILES!

YOU **ARE!** YOU **ARE!**

THOSE ARE **RELATED** BUSINESSES.

A KRUSTYBURGER EXPRESS, A KRUSTACO HUT AND A P.J. MACKRUSTYDOODLES.

YOU **CHEATED** ME!

LISTEN, I'M JUST A COLORFUL **SHILL**. YOU NEED TO SPEAK TO MY **LEGAL** BRAIN.

DREDERICK!

DON'T **FORCE** ME TO HARM YOU, SIR.

STINKING, BACKSTABBING, MONKEY-LOVIN' **CHEAT!**

PUNCH IT, MR TEENY.

AWWWW...THIS SHOULD HAVE BEEN THE **HAPPIEST** DAY OF MY LIFE. HOW CAN I MAKE MONEY WITH THREE **OTHER** KRUSTYS TO COMPETE WITH?

IT'S NOT **THAT** BAD, HOMIE. YOU JUST HAVE TO WORK HARD TO MAKE YOUR KRUSTYBURGER THE **BEST** ONE EVER.

WORK HARD? THAT'S FOR **IMMIGRANTS.**

BUT YOUR PLACE COULD BE *BETTER* THAN THE KRUSTY'S ON THE OTHER CORNERS.

NO IT *CAN'T*, MARGE!

GRAND OP

THAT'S JUST THE *DEFEATEST* IN YOU TALKING.

TO PREVENT COMPETITION BETWEEN FRANCHISES, THEY ALL HAVE TO BE EXACTLY THE SAME.

IT'S ALL IN THIS *BINDER* THAT I PRETENDED TO READ BEFORE SIGNING AWAY ALL OF OUR FUTURES.

YOU'RE *RIGHT*, DAD.

THIS IS A MANIFESTO THAT LEGALLY *BINDS* THE OWNER TO LEVELS OF *MEDIOCRITY* THE PUBLIC SCHOOL SYSTEM COULD ONLY *DREAM* OF.

IT SAYS IF YOU MAKE *ANY* IMPROVEMENTS, YOU LOSE THE RESTAURANT *AND* THE MONEY WE PUT INTO IT.

YOU'RE SMART, LISA. YOU INVENTED *VELCRO*.

NO I *DIDN'T*.

YOU SHOWED ME HOW TO *USE* VELCRO.

WHAT DO YOU *WANT* FROM ME?

YOU'RE OUR ONLY *HOPE!* READ THE MANUAL. *STUDY* IT!

BUT *WHY?*

A *LOOPHOLE!* FIND ME A *LOOPHOLE!*

DAD, IF THE RULES ARE THAT YOU CAN'T MAKE THE PLACE *BETTER* WITHOUT LOSING OUR SHIRTS...

...WHAT IF YOU MADE IT *WORSE*?

LISA?

HMM...I THINK BART IS RIGHT FOR ONCE. AMAZINGLY, THERE'S NOTHING IN HERE THAT SAYS YOU CAN'T DRIVE A KRUSTY BURGER INTO THE GROUND.

THEN THAT'S IT! I'LL *PROVE* TO THAT TWO-FACED FUNNYMAN THAT *NOBODY* CAN CUT CORNERS AND LOWER STANDARDS LIKE HOMER J. SIMPSON!

I'LL *SHOW* THEM THAT THEY'VE OVERESTIMATED ME FOR THE *LAST* TIME!

WE'LL PUT MORE *CEREAL* IN THE BURGER-MEAT!

WE'LL *REUSE* STRAWS AND NAPKINS!

WE'LL TRAIN *SEAGULLS* TO CLEAN TABLES!

WE WILL BOLDLY GO WHERE NO LOWERED EXPECTATION HAS GONE BEFORE!

YOU DA *MAN*, HOMER!

BWAH-HA HA-HA-HA HA-HA!

THAT ONE *NEVER* GETS TIRED.

HEY, I THOUGHT THAT WAS ONE OF YOUR *FAVES*, LIS.

RECENT EVENTS HAVE CAUSED ME TO LOSE MY ZEST FOR LIFE.

WHATEVER.

♪DING♪ DONG!

I'LL GET IT.

HUH?

LUNCHLADY *DORIS*? WHAT ARE *YOU* DOING HERE?

THE SCHOOL BOARD *FIRED* ME WHEN THE CLOWN TOOK OVER THE CAFETERIA.

BUT I GOT A JOB WITH KATIE KATE KOSMETICS, SO I'M *STILL* IN THE ANIMAL BY-PRODUCTS BUSINESS.

I THINK I MAY BE ABLE TO *HELP* YOU.

BY *ORDERING* SOME LADY BOTOX WRINKLE-RECTIFIER?

NOT *EXACTLY*...

LATER...

SO, WHAT MAKES YOU THINK *YOU'RE* KRUSTYBURGER MATERIAL?

HELP WANTED

I'M *PEOPLE*-ORIENTED. I *ENJOY* THE SMELL OF RANCID GREASE. I HAVE LITTLE OR *NO* SELF-ESTEEM.

HEY, *WAIT* A SECOND--

AREN'T YOU THE GUY WHO *SOLD* ME THIS PLACE?

HAVE A *HEART*, PAL! OL' GIL *NEEDS* THIS JOB!

OUT!

WHAT'S GIL GONNA DO *NOW*? I CAN'T SELL ANY MORE BLOOD.

LET THE *CLOWN* TURN THAT SMILE UPSIDE DOWN.

HAVE A *FREE* KRUSTY-COLA.

FREE *SODA*?

THAT'S SUPPOSED TO MAKE THINGS *BETTER*?

CRUSH!

GIL *NEVER* GETS A BREAK.

YOU'RE THE MILLION DOLLAR WINNER!

WHO WOULD'VE THOUGHT THAT RUNNING A **CRUMMY** RESTAURANT WOULD BE AS MUCH WORK AS RUNNING A **GOOD** ONE!

I NEED TO FIND AN EMPLOYEE WHO SHARES MY CRAPPY VISION BEFORE I--

I UNDERSTAND YOU HAVE AN **OPENING**.

DON'T I **KNOW** YOU?

I **RESCUED** YOU FROM THE BEANIE WIENIE TROUGH LAST PARENTS NIGHT.

AND I'VE **CURSED** YOUR FOUL NAME EVER SINCE...

...**WHO-EVER** YOU ARE.

MR SIMPSON, I'M THE ANSWER TO YOUR **PRAYERS**.

YUH-YEAH?

YOU **THINK** YOU'VE LOWERED YOUR STANDARDS AS FAR AS THEY CAN GO, BUT YOU **HAVEN'T**.

THERE ARE LUH-**LOWER** STANDARDS?

GOVERNMENT STANDARDS, MR SIMPSON.

GOVERNMENT STANDARDS.

I DON'T KNOW WHAT *YOU* CAN DO, LADY. I'VE DONE EVERY-THING I *CAN* TO MAKE THIS PLACE A DUMP.

LOCKING THE REST ROOMS. *CIGARETTES* IN THE KID'S MEALS. *CELINE DION* ON THE SOUND SYSTEM...

...AND KRUSTY HASN'T EVEN NOTICED!

YOU HAVE A LOT OF *IMAGINATION* FOR AN AMATEUR, SIMPSON. I'LL *GIVE* YOU THAT.

THE *ROACHES* ARE A NICE TOUCH.

I NAMED *THAT* ONE "CRAWLY."

BUT THERE'S SO MUCH *MORE* YOU COULD DO.

AND, AS SOMEONE WHO INCREASED THE *BAG* LUNCH-TO-*BOUGHT* LUNCH RATIO TO AN 80-20 SPLIT...

...I'M YOUR *MAN*.

BUT HOW WILL WE *DO* IT? *HOW?*

TWO LITTLE WORDS.

MILITARY.

SURPLUS.

UM... GREAT.

BUT CAN YOU *LOSE* THE CREEPY FLASHLIGHT?

NO.

OH-KAY.

SOON...

MILITARY ANTIQUES

DON'T GET MUCH *CALL* FOR THIS STUFF...

...ESPECIALLY IN THESE QUANTITIES.

WELL, I *LOST* MY PENTAGON CONTACTS.

TELL ME ABOUT IT. YOU GOTTA GO TO EASTERN EUROPE FOR *DECENT* FRAG GRENADES THESE DAYS.

BUT I *SHOULD* BE ABLE TO HOOK YOU UP.

ANYHOO, I GOT YOUR CASES OF G.I. TUNA, BULLY BEEF, AND GIZZARD LOAF--

BULLY BEEF

BULLY BEEF

EEF

HEY, *SKINNER*. YOU GONNA *BUY* SOMETHING? THIS AIN'T A *COSTUME* PARADE.

SORRY. I GOT *LOST* IN THE MOMENT.

DAD, I THINK THIS MEAT'S GONE *BAD*.

IT SMELLS LIKE OUR *SOFA*. AND THE *LID* IS RUSTY.

AND ISN'T THERE A *LAW* AGAINST CHILD LABOR?

JUST EMPTY THE CANS IN THE GRINDER AND *NONE* OF YOUR SASS.

YEAH, IT SMELLS LIKE *SASS*, TOO.

AND NOT ANOTHER *WORD* ABOUT CHILD LABOR LAWS, BOY.

C'MON, THOSE FRIES AREN'T GOING TO PULL *THEMSELVES* OUT, MAGGIE!

THANK YOU FOR YOUR *ORDER,* SIR.

HEY, THIS ISN'T A KRUSTY-SACK. IT'S AN *AIR SICKNESS* BAG.

FOR USE IN CASE OF AIRSICKNESS

WE GET 'EM *CHEAP.* AND BESIDES...

...YOU MIGHT *NEED* IT.

HWOOP!

HWAAAAHP!

HWUPP!

DORIS, I THINK HIRING *YOU* WAS THE SMARTEST THING I'VE DONE SINCE I STOPPED WATCHING *"FRIENDS."*

WELL, *HERE* COMES THE COUP DE GRACE, MR. SIMPSON.

HWHERP!

THAT'S NOT KOOK DEGRASS!

IT'S THE *HEALTH INSPECTOR!*

PSST! REMEMBER WHAT I *TOLD* YOU.

OH. OH YEAHHH...

YOU THE *OWNER?* I HAVE YOUR *REPORT* HERE.

YOU CAN STAY OPEN, BUT YOU'RE GONNA HAVE TO MAKE SOME *CHANGES* TO--

HUH?

HEY, PAL. CAN'T WE WORK SOMETHING OUT?

LIKE A BIG 'N KRUSTY WITH *EXTRA* LETTUCE.

LETTUCE. *GET* IT?

LETTUCE?

SURE *THING,* BUDDY. FOR THAT YOU GET A *TRIPLE* "A" RATING.

IT'S NOT WORKING! HE'S *TAKING* THE BRIBE! DO SOMETHING!

OH *NO!* I I--

POW!

UNNH!

YOU'RE *NUTS,* MISTER! I WANT THIS PLACE *PADLOCKED!* MANIAC!

YES!

YOU GUYS, AGAIN? WITH THE NUMBERS AND ALL THAT GESCHEFT, YOU MAKE ME FARBLONDGET!

MR KRUSTY...

...YOU CAN SIT THERE AND MAKE UP WORDS OR LISTEN TO THESE PROJECTIONS.

THERE'S A PROBLEM WITH STORE #987976.

SO, ONE JOINT IS FALLING BEHIND.

IT'S MORE THAN THAT. THE PERFORMANCE OF #987976 IS CREATING A NEGATIVE SAME-STORE RECIDIVISM FOR THE ENTIRE AREA.

WE FORWARD LOOK A FREEFALL PROFIT TERMINIZING WITH SHIFTS TO THE MINUS COLUMN IN GEOMETRICAL PROGRESSION.

WHAT'S SO BAD ABOUT WHAT THE GUY WHO RUNS STORE #99-WHATSIS DID?

IN ENGLISH?

HE HOCKED A LOOGIE IN THE PUNCHBOWL, KRUSTY!

AND SOMEBODY'S GONNA HAVE TO LADLE IT OUT!

OW!

ALL RIGHT! ALL RIGHT!

IT'S TIME FOR OPERATION LOOGIE LADLE!

THIRTY MINUTES LATER...

YOU *KNOW,* MR SIMPSON, THAT CONGEALED FRYER FAT YOU'RE DRINKING ISN'T EXACTLY *EDIBLE.*

FOR *HUMANS* ANYWAY.

WHO *CARES?*

I THOUGHT OUR PROBLEMS WERE SOLVED, BUT MY BRILLIANT SCHEME HAD A FATAL FLAW!

EVEN THOUGH KRUSTY OWES ME MY MONEY BACK, I'M *STILL* LIABLE FOR ALL *THE BILLS!* AND THEY TOTAL *TWICE* WHAT I PAID THAT CLOWN.

FINAL NOTICE FOR REAL

FINAL NOTICE

FINAL, FINAL NOTICE, STUPID.

WHAT'S THAT HORRIBLE *WHUPPING* SOUND?

UNLESS I *WASTED* MY TIME IN THE NATIONAL GUARD I'D SAY THAT'S...

WHUP! WHUP! WHUP! WHUP! WHUP! WHUP!

...INCOMING!

WHUP! WHUP! WHUP! WHUP! WHUP! WHUP!

KRRUUNCH!

SO *THAT'S* WHY THERE WAS A BIG HOOK ON THE ROOF.

BUT HOW WILL THEY EXPLAIN *THIS* AWAY?

WHAM!

LOOK OUT!

FUTURE HOME OF A BRAND-NEW KRUSTYBURGER

NO, THERE WASN'T A KRUSTYBURGER HERE BEFORE. YOU MUST BE THINKING OF "CRUSTY BERGER."

THAT'S HOW.

YOU CAN'T ARGUE THAT IT'S NOT *DIRECT.*

THE NEXT AFTERNOON...

WHERE'S HOMER?

YOUR FATHER'S OUT GETTING A *SECOND JOB* TO PAY THE CREDITORS.

WELL, AT LEAST WE CAN ALL GET BACK TO EATING HEALTHY.

AND I'LL HAVE TO GO BACK TO *PAYING* TO GET MY DAILY PERCENTAGE OF TRIGLYCERIDES.

THAT'S YOUR FATHER'S CAR I HEAR, KIDS.

LET'S ALL MEET HIM AT THE FRONT DOOR AND SHOW OUR SUPPORT.

SURE.

WHY NOT THROW HIM A BONE?

HELLO, HONEY! HOW WAS THE JOB HUNT?

OKAY, I GUESS.

NOW, DOES ANYONE HERE HAVE "PROBLEM SKIN?"

THE END

MATT GROENING PRESENTS

HOTFOOT IN THE PARK

IAN BOOTHBY	PHIL ORTIZ	MIKE DECARLO	ART VILLANUEVA	KAREN BATES	BILL MORRISON
STORY	PENCILS	INKS	COLORS	LETTERS	EDITOR

LATER...

WINNER

ALL *RIGHT!* BART SIMPSON SCORES AGAIN! WHY ISN'T THIS AN OLYMPIC SPORT?

WHAT CAN I GET FOR ALL THESE?

HERE YOU GO!

WHAT? I SPENT TWENTY DOLLARS, AND ALL I GET IS A FIVE CENT WHISTLE IN THE SHAPE OF A WOMAN'S HEAD?

NOT JUST *ANY* WOMAN. THAT'S *ERIN BROCKOVICH,* AMERICA'S MOST BELOVED WHISTLE BLOWER!

YOU'RE DOING IT ALL WRONG, SIMPSON. IT'S ALL IN THE *WRIST.* WATCH!

WHAT A RIP OFF!

WHACK! THE BALL

SEE? ALL IN THE WRIST!

SO, LITTLE LADY, HOW MANY JELLY BEANS DO YOU THINK ARE IN THIS HERE JAR?

LET'S SEE, IT'S A STANDARD 40 OUNCE MASON PICKLING JAR SO TAKING INTO ACCOUNT THE HEIGHT AND DIAMETER...

THREE HUNDRED SIXTY FOUR.

UH... YEAH, THAT'S RIGHT!

HOT DOGS

YOU GOT *LUCKY!*

NO, I'VE JUST BEEN GETTING A LITTLE EXTRA TUTORING AFTER SCHOOL FROM *THE MATHEMAGICIAN*.

AND NOW FOR A TRICK I CALL "THE DISAPPEARING REMAINDER." PICK A FLASH CARD, ANY FLASH CARD!

MAYBE LATER.

POP A BALLOON for 25¢

251 × 119

5⟌25,175

16² ÷ 118

KNOC

OKAY, DOUBLE OR NOTHING! HOW MANY PICKLED EGGS?

HMMM...

ONE HUNDRED SEVEN EGGS!

HMM...

NINE HUNDRED EIGHTY SEVEN PEANUTS!

GRRR...

EIGHTY-TWO PIG'S FEET! EEEEW!

HEY, WHAT THE--? I WAS JUST WALKING BY!

GRAN
PRIZ

2"
PR

WELL, IF YOU'RE OUT OF DOLLS, I'LL BE GETTING THESE OVER TO THE TOY DONATION BIN AT THE SPRINGFIELD ORPHANAGE.

NO, WAIT! I AIN'T NEVER LOST TO A RUBE BEFORE!

GIVE ME ONE LAST CHANCE TO DEFEND MY CARNEY HONOR. IF YOU WIN, I'LL...I'LL GIVE YOU *THE FAIR* ITSELF!

REALLY?

ALL YOU HAVE TO DO IS GUESS HOW MANY JARS ARE IN THE *MEGA JAR!* AND HOW MANY OBJECTS ARE IN *THEM!*

:GASP!:

THE NEXT DAY... 'S DUNGEON SEBALL CARD SHOP

"TAKE ME TO YOUR COMIC BOOKS & BASEBALL CARDS"

YES WE'RE OPEN

507

I WANT TO COMPLAIN!

YOU WANT TO COMPLAIN? LOOK AT ME! THESE VULCAN EARS I HAD SURGICALLY ATTACHED DO NOT MATCH. I LOOK LIKE A FOOL.

WHEN DID YOU GET THAT DONE?

I APPEARED ON THE NEW FOX SERIES "EXTREME NERD MAKE-OVER!"

WOW! THIS IS COOL. BUT HOW ARE YOU GOING TO REATTACH MY REAL ARM LATER?

RIGHT, YOUR ARM. UM...ER...

ANYWAY, WHEN I BOUGHT THIS COMIC IT PROMISED FREE CARNIVAL RIDES! BUT LOOK AT THE FINE PRINT!

I SHALL DO SO AFTER I RETRIEVE THIS MR. FANTASTIC ACTION FIGURE THAT IS STUCK IN A DRIED PUDDLE OF MR. PIBB.

FWOOSH!

OLD DRY COMICS

ESIGHE I FEAR THIS WILL REQUIRE A TEAM UP WITH MR. CLEAN!

GAH!

OLD DRY COMICS

OILY RAGS

INEVITABLY...

MY SHOP! MY FORTRESS OF SOLITUDE! MY *SANCTUM SANCTORUM!*

AND *YOU!* YOU DID *NOTHING!*

YEAH, SORRY. WE WERE HIRED FOR OUR LOOKS!

WE'RE NO GOOD WITH FIRE, BUT, MAN, CAN WE SELL CALENDARS!

NO ONE EVEN KNOWS HOW TO DRIVE THE TRUCK. WE HAD TO PUSH IT ALL THE WAY HERE!

MARCH

I'M REALLY SORRY ALL THIS HAPPENED.

NOT AS SORRY AS YOU'RE GOING TO BE WHEN I SUE YOU FOR EVERY PENNY IN YOUR PIGGY BANK!

FOR YEARS I HAVE STUDIED THE METHODS OF LAWYERS WHO ARE ALSO SUPERHEROES. THIS IS MY CHANCE TO UTILIZE THOSE LEGAL SKILLS AND AMAZE EVERYONE!

COMIC BOOK GUY, YOU *AMAZE* ME!

I HAVE NEVER SEEN A MORE *AMAZING* WASTE OF THE COURT'S TIME!

PLEASE, YOUR HONOR, I REQUIRE SILENCE. I AM TRYING TO HEAR HIS HEART-BEAT TO TELL IF HE'S LYING OR NOT!

I CAN HEAR HOMER'S HEARTBEAT, BUT THAT'S JUST BECAUSE OF HIS HIGH BLOOD PRESSURE FROM YEARS OF ARTERY-CLOGGING JUNK FOOD.

THUMP! THUMP! THUMP!

WELL, I'LL SHOW YOU! I'M GOING TO GO ON A DIET AND START EXERCISING TOMORROW!

THUMP! THUMP! KA-THUMP!

KA-THUMP! KA-THUMP!

LIAR.

THE COURT FINDS IN FAVOR OF BART SIMPSON AND ORDERS THE BAILIFF TO MAKE COMIC BOOK GUY'S EARS NORMAL AGAIN! THEY REALLY CREEP ME OUT!

BANG!

NOW WHERE WILL I GO? WHAT WILL I DO? I FEEL AS USELESS AS FOX MULDER'S REPLACEMENT IN THE LAST SEASON OF "THE X-FILES."

WELL, I *DO* FEEL BAD THAT THIS HAPPENED. LOOK, I'VE GOT AN IDEA...

WILL LITIGATE FOR FOOD

MRS. KRABAPPEL, PRINCIPAL SKINNER? YOU'RE WORKING HERE?

LISA OFFERED US PART-TIME WORK. WITH RECENT CUTBACKS TO TEACHER'S SALARIES I NEED A SECOND JOB TO MAKE ENDS MEET.

AND I NEED THE MONEY TO BUY SHOES BECAUSE MOTHER WON'T RAISE MY ALLOWANCE.

WHEEEE! I'M A NUMERATOR!

WHEEEE! I'M A DENOMINATOR!

THE FRACTION RIDE

WOW, LISA! I'M IMPRESSED!

3

5

IS THERE A "TUNNEL OF LOVE"?

NO, BUT THERE'S THE "TUNNEL OF JUST WANTING TO BE FRIENDS"!

TUNNEL OF JUST WANTING TO BE FRIENDS

≡SIGH≡

HEY! I WAS TOLD WE HAVE TO PASS A POP QUIZ TO RIDE THE ROLLER-COASTER.

IT'S TRUE! AT LISALAND THE RIDES YOU EARN ARE BECAUSE YOU LEARN!

YOUR GRADE MUST BE THIS HIGH TO RIDE ↓

A
B
C
D
F

ELSEWHERE...

I'M JUST SAYING. THIS TOWN NEEDS A *REAL* FIRE DEPARTMENT. IT'S A *SAFETY* ISSUE!

LOOK, ARE YOU GONNA TALK ALL NIGHT OR PLAY "FLAMING AXE DARTS"?

Y'KNOW, HE'S RIGHT. THIS PLACE HERE'S BURNED TO THE GROUND FIVE TIMES SINCE I TOOK IT OVER. AND ONLY THREE OF THEM FIRES WAS INSURANCE SCAMS!

YEAH, BUT WHAT ARE YA GONNA DO?

I GOT AN IDEA! WOW, AND THEY SAID MY ALCOHOL-DAMAGED BRAIN CELLS WOULDN'T *EVER* GROW BACK!

MAYOR QUIMBY?

WHAT?! IS MY WIFE HERE?

THE NEXT DAY...

WOW! SO WE'RE ALL *REAL* FIREFIGHTERS?

I GET TO PICK MY TEAM AND YOU GUYS WERE THE BEST OF THE BEST.

ALSO, IT WAS LATE, AND YOU WERE ALL IN THE ROOM AT THE TIME.

I JUST WISH *THEM* JERKS HADN'T TAKEN OVER THE FIREHOUSE!

JERKS? I'M GONNA BLAST HIM WITH MY PROTON PACK! I AIN'T AFRAID O' NO MOES!

HE'S NOT WORTH IT, RAY. JUST GO TO YOUR HAPPY PLACE.

I'VE BEEN THINKING. THE PROBLEM WITH FIRE-FIGHTERS IS THEY ONLY SHOW UP AFTER A FIRE *STARTS*.

WE HAVE TO FIGHT FIRES *BEFORE* THEY START!

OH YEAH? HOW?

COMING THROUGH! RANDOM FIRE PREVENTION!

TRY NOT TO INHALE THE FOAM! WE COULDN'T AFFORD THE NON-TOXIC KIND!

OCH! BUT WILLIE'S ALREADY HAD A BATH THIS YEAR!

GAH!

PSSSSH!

FWOOOOSH!

WHAAA?

PSSSSH!

you are now leaving **SPRINGFIELD**

WHAT'S THIS ALL ABOUT?

IT'S ALL ABOUT FIRE SAFETY. YOU TOOK TWENTY MINUTES TO CLEAR THE TOWN. IF THIS HAD BEEN AN ACTUAL FIRE, YOU'D ALL BE CRISPY BACON BY NOW!

MMM...CRISPY BACON.

AND YOU SAY THEY DO THIS KIND OF THING A LOT IN THIS TOWN?

THE AVERAGE IS THREE STUPID THINGS A WEEK. I'D FEEL *BAD* ABOUT TAKING ADVANTAGE EXCEPT FOR *ONE THING*.

WHAT'S THAT?

I'M CRIMINAL SCUM!

77

LATER...

OH SWEET HEAVENS!

WILLIE, YOU'VE BEEN WARNED. EITHER WEAR UNDERPANTS OR STOP GETTING ON THAT RIDE!

SOLAR SYSTEM SWING

PRINCIPAL SKIM MILK?

IT'S SKINNER, RALPH. WHAT'S WRONG?

I GOT A "D" ON THIS TEST. CAN I STILL GO ON THE RADIUS-GO-ROUND?

I'M SORRY, BUT NO, RALPH. RULES ARE RULES.

LOOK AT THE BABY! TOO DUMB TO PASS A SIMPLE TEST!

C'MON, HURRY UP WITH OUR EXAMS!

;SOB!;

HOMER, WHAT ARE YOU DOING? IS THAT HOUSE PAINT?

WE NEED A FIRE DOG, MARGE. FOR MORALE.

DON'T WORRY, AS LONG AS HE DOESN'T LICK HIMSELF, HE'LL BE FINE!

I DON'T WANT YOU PAINTING OUR DOG!

¦HISSS¦

FINE, THEN *YOU* TALK THE CAT DOWN FROM THE BOOKCASE.

HOMEY, YOU KNOW I SUPPORT YOU IN WHATEVER YOU DO, AND I'M PROUD OF YOU.

BUT YOUR FIRE SAFETY IDEAS ARE GETTING A LITTLE EXTREME.

OH, EXTREME, AM I?

WELL, WAIT UNTIL THERE'S A *REAL FIRE!* WE'LL SEE WHO'S LAUGHING *THEN!*

HOMER, THERE'S A REAL FIRE. COME QUICK!

I'LL BE RIGHT THERE. I JUST HAVE TO DO ONE THING.

HA! HA! HA!

¦SIGH¦

SO WHADDA WE DO NOW?

YEAH, ALL WE KNOW IS FIRE *PREVENTION*. WE DON'T KNOW HOW TO *FIGHT* A FIRE.

WELL, YOU KNOW WHAT THEY SAY!

FIGHT FIRE *WITH* FIRE!

SOON...

OKAY, *THAT* DOESN'T SEEM TO BE WORKING.

WHY DID YOU HAVE A FLAME-THROWER, MOE?

AW, I JUST USE IT IN THE BAR TO KEEP RATS AWAY. AND THE IRISH.

THE WHOLE FAIR IS ON FIRE! WE'RE *TRAPPED!*

HOT DOGS

WHY DO WE ALWAYS LISTEN TO HIS DUMB IDEAS?

IT'S HIS *CHARISMA!* I'D LIKE TO GOUGE IT OUT WITH A SHARPENED SPOON!

IT WORKED!

I GUESS WHAT PEOPLE SAY IS TRUE. THIS TOWN REALLY *DOES* BLOW!

RALPHIE! YOU SAVED EVERYONE! AND YOUR PANTS STAYED BONE DRY DOING IT! I'M SO PROUD OF YOU!

YOU'VE EARNED A TREAT. WHAT SAY I TAKE YOU TO THE STATION AND LET YOU SMACK THE PERPS AROUND WITH A PHONE BOOK?

I'D RATHER STAY HERE AND PLAY. BUT I'M NOT SMART ENOUGH TO GO ON THE RIDES.

RALPH, I'M SORRY. I GOT SO WRAPPED UP IN WHAT *I* WANTED THAT I FORGOT THAT FAIRS SHOULD BE FOR EVERYONE.

AND NOW *NO ONE* CAN GO ON THE RIDES.

WAIT! I'M GETTING ANOTHER IDEA!

WELL, WHAT *IS* IT?

THE NEXT WEEK...

welcome to RALF-LAND

YOU GAVE THE FAIR TO RALPH? IS THAT A GOOD IDEA? I MEAN HE SPELLED HIS OWN NAME WRONG ON THE SIGN!

THE RIDES WERE ALL RUINED ANYWAY, AND IT MADE HIM SO HAPPY.

I HEARD THEY CALL IT RALF-LAND BECAUSE THAT'S WHAT ALL THE RIDES MAKE YOU DO!

HOT DOGS

85

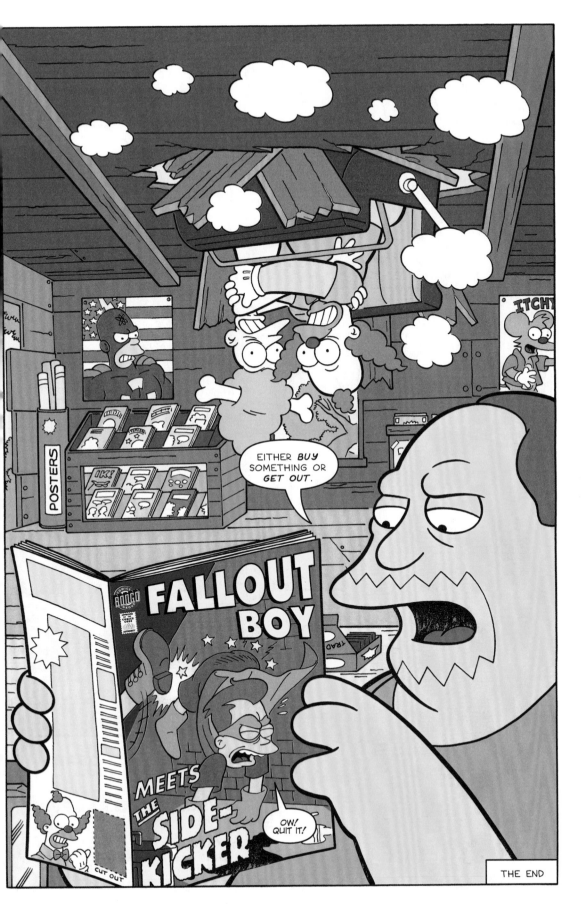

JUST SIGN IT, AND OL' GIL WILL START WORK AS YOUR *BANKRUPTCY* LAWYER! C'MON, I NEED THIS. I DON'T EVEN HAVE ENOUGH MONEY TO BUY POMADE TO KEEP MY COWLICKS DOWN!

I DON'T KNOW. MAYBE THINGS'LL TURN AROUND. THE ECONOMY CAN'T STAY BAD FOREVER.

THE WOLF'S AT EVERYONE'S DOOR NOWADAYS.

SEE?

BOOTLEG RICKY'S ~~RECORDS~~ MP3s

DO YOU HAVE THE NEW WHITESNAKE DOWNLOAD?

IT'LL TAKE FIVE MINUTES. I ONLY GOT A *DIAL-UP* MAN.

4 2 3 FLAVOR ICE CREAM

VANILLA AND UNREFRIGERATED VANILLA.

BED, BATH AND *Boudoir*

DO YOU HAVE ANY WITH LESS *HAIR* ON THEM?

ASK ABOUT OUR USED HOTEL SOAP

I CAN THROW IN A *RAZOR* FOR A *BUCK*.

YES, TIMES ARE HARD FOR EVERYONE, WITH MERCHANTS HAVING TO FIND NEW SOURCES OF INCOME...

GREETINGS, GENTLE ELDERS, AND BEHOLD THE FUTURE...

SPRINGFIELD RETIREMENT CASTLE

...THE FUTURE OF *DISCOUNT FUNERALS!*

WHY PAY FUNERAL PARLOR PRICES FOR A COFFIN WHEN FOR JUST PENNIES ON THE DOLLAR, YOU CAN ENJOY ETERNITY IN AN ANDROID'S DUNGEON COMIC BOOK BOX?

IS THAT SANTA? IS IT CHRISTMAS ALREADY?

THIS ACID-FREE, DUST-REPELLANT, OVERSIZED BOX WAS DESIGNED TO HOLD THE EXTRA LARGE TREASURY EDITION CROSSOVERS OF THE 1970s.

THE FORMAT FAILED TO CATCH ON, AND SO I AM PASSING THE SAVINGS ONTO YOU!

RADIOACTIVE MAN MEETS BUCKY BUCKS RICHEST BOY ON EARTH

BUT WHAT IF WE WANT TO BE *CREMATED*?

MAYBE IT'D BE NICE TO BE WARM FOR ONCE!

THEN FORGET THE URN AND HAVE YOUR ASHES PRESERVED IN ONE OF OUR VERY AFFORDABLE *MYLAR COMIC BAGS!*

REMEMBER OUR MOTTO, "A PENNY IS *SAVED* WHEN YOU'RE NOT *URNED!*"

93

TIMES ARE TOUGH FOR ALL OF US, BUT WE'VE GOT TO HAVE FAITH THAT THE *BIG MAN'S* GOING TO HELP US!

DON'T LOOK AT *ME*. MY SHOP DECLARED *BANKRUPTCY* THIS MORNING!

SO WHAT ARE WE SUPPOSED TO DO NOW?

IF WE DON'T THINK OF SOMETHING, OUR BUSINESSES ARE GOING TO LAST ABOUT AS LONG AS A NEW JOHN LARROQUETTE SIT-COM!

I CALL FIRST DIBS ON JUMPING OUT THE WINDOW!

FOR *SHAME!*

LIKE MY DISCOUNT HEAT-LAMP HOT DOGS, YOU ALL MAKE ME *SICK!* HOW CAN YOU GIVE UP HOPE?!

THIS IS A LAND OF *OPPORTUNITY!*

THAT IS EASY FOR YOU TO SAY, AMIGO! YOUR KWIK-E-MART BUSINESS *THRIVES* WHILE OURS *FAIL!*

THIS IS TRUE, SEÑOR DING DONG, BUT ASK YOURSELVES THIS. *WHY* IS MY BUSINESS SO SUCCESSFUL?

THE ADDICTIVE TRACE ELEMENTS OF CAFFEINE, NICOTINE, AND OPIUM YOU LACE YOUR SQUISHEES WITH, PERHAPS?

UM...WELL, YES, BUT MORE THAN THAT IS MY **COMMITMENT** TO MY CUSTOMERS!

I AM OPEN **TWENTY-FOUR** HOURS A DAY, **SEVEN** DAYS A WEEK!

YOUR NINE-TO-FIVE HOURS DON'T **CALCUTTA IT** IN TODAY'S TWENTY-FOUR HOUR WORLD!

BY CLOSING AT NIGHT YOU ARE MISSING OUT ON THREE **KEY IMPULSE BUYING** CUSTOMERS.

THE INSOMNIACS! MEN WHO HAVE HAD A FIGHT WITH THEIR WIVES AND BEEN KICKED OUT! AND **VAMPIRES**!

HE'S RIGHT! I DON'T **WANT** TO WEAR THIS **TUXEDO** EVERY DAY, BUT THE **SWEATER VEST** STORE IS CLOSED AT NIGHT!

ALL IN FAVOR OF MAKING ALL SPRINGFIELD BUSINESSES OPEN TWENTY-FOUR HOURS, SAY "AYE!"

"AYE!"

SPRINGFIELD TOWN HALL

TONIGHT-SPRINGFIELD MERCHANT'S ASSOCIATION
TOMORROW-HUMAN CANNONBALL CONVENTION

95

THE NEXT NIGHT...

WHIRRR!

BEEP!

HONK!

WOW, LOOK AT THE CITY! IT'S SO BRIGHT AND LOUD! IT'S HARD TO BELIEVE IT'S 11 P.M.!

ALL THE LIGHT IS REALLY CONFUSING THE BIRDS

MAYOR QUIMBY PASSED THE LAW EARLIER TODAY. *ALL* SPRINGFIELD BUSINESSES ARE NOW OPEN TWENTY-FOUR HOURS A DAY, SO THE LIGHT AND NOISE ISN'T *EVER* GOING TO GO AWAY!

WHY ARE YOU TELLING ME ALL THIS? I ALREADY KNOW.

I WAS JUST FILLING IN *THE READERS!*

HUH?

HELLO, LISA, WE'RE YOUR NEW NEIGHBORS, THE *READER* FAMILY. I'M BILL READER, THIS IS MY WIFE EMILY, AND OUR BABY BECKY ANN. THANKS FOR KEEPING US UP TO SPEED, BART!

97

MEANWHILE...

OPENING CHEVRON 9 OF THE STARGATE!

UH–OH.

WHAT?

I HAVEN'T SLEPT IN SO LONG I'VE FORGOTTEN WHICH ONE OF US IS *PATTY* AND WHICH IS *SELMA*.

ME, TOO.

AND THE NEXT DAY, AT SPRINGFIELD ELEMENTARY...

I'M ACTUALLY *ENJOYING* THE LACK OF SLEEP. I'VE BEEN GETTING A LOT MORE HOMEWORK DONE, AND SO FAR THERE'VE BEEN NO ILL EFFECTS. AT THIS RATE, I CAN EVEN *SKIP* A FEW GRADES AND...

UH... LISA?

DON'T INTERRUPT, BART. I'M TALKING TO BART!

"WHO IS THAT YELLOW *DYNAMO*, SMITHERS?"

THUD!

THAT'S HOMER SIMPSON, SIR, ONE OF THE MOSS GATHERERS HERE IN SECTION 7G, BUT I'VE *NEVER* SEEN HIM WORK SO HARD.

CLICK! CLICK! CLICK! CLICK! CLICK! CLICK!

HAZARD

NO SOLICITORS

DANGER

IN THE LAST FEW DAYS, HE'S *TRIPLED* PLANT EFFICIENCY. THAT ADDED TO THE TOWN'S INCREASED ENERGY USE, AND YOU'RE WELL ON YOUR WAY TO GOING FROM FILTHY RICH TO FILTHY *STINKING* RICH, SIR!

EXCELLENT! THAT REMINDS ME, IT'S TIME FOR MY *MONEY BATH!*

I'LL BE RIGHT IN TO WARM UP THE *SILVER DOLLARS* FOR YOU, SIR!

I JUST DON'T UNDERSTAND IT. NORMALLY, SIMPSON WOULD HAVE CAUSED A *MELTDOWN* OR AT LEAST A *TOXIC SPILL* BY THIS TIME OF DAY!

CLICK! CLICK!

¡GASP!¡ HE'S *FAST ASLEEP!*

SO WHEN HE'S SLEEP-WALKING, SIMPSON IS A MODEL EMPLOYEE. *FASCINATING!*

CLICK! CLICK! CLICK! CLICK!

"WE NOW JOIN 'MCWIGGUM' ALREADY IN PROGRESS!"

BLAM! BLAM!

HE'S OPENED FIRE, CHIEF!

YOU GOT *THAT* RIGHT, *FUNK SOUL BROTHER!*

WHAT?

IT'S EASIER TO JUST *GO ALONG* WITH IT!

LISTEN, PUNK! I DIG WHERE YOU'RE COMING FROM! YOU'RE HEADING FOR A *DISCO INFERNO,* AND YOU NEED TO *TAKE A CHANCE ON ME* IF YOU WANT TO BE *STAYIN' ALIVE!*

DUDE! THAT'S WHAT YOU COPS *ALWAYS* SAY!

BLAM! BLAM!

MEANWHILE...

I CAN'T BELIEVE HOW MUCH I'VE BEEN ABLE TO DO WITHOUT SLEEP GETTING IN MY WAY. I'VE READ EVERY BOOK IN THE SCHOOL LIBRARY!

HOW ARE *YOU* DOING, BART?

FINE. NO HALLUCINATIONS AT ALL!

12500

HEY, WHAT'S THAT NUMBER DOING THERE? IT LOOKS LIKE A *VIDEO GAME* SCORE.

WHAT ARE *YOU* TALKING ABOUT?

BART! YOU'VE GOT TO BEAT KRUSTY TO THE KRUSTYBURGER RESTAURANT TO OPEN THE BONUS LEVEL!

12500

I NEED THAT *BONUS!* I'LL TAKE WILLIE'S TRACTOR!

13000

OH, APU, THE TOWN CAN'T TAKE BEING OPEN TWENTY-FOUR HOURS A DAY!

NO CHECKS CREDIT CARDS FOOD STAMPS

OH, DO NOT WORRY, LISA. IT JUST TAKES A WHILE, BUT SOON THEY WILL *ADJUST* TO THE LACK OF SLEEP.

WHY! HEH, HEH, FOR A WHILE I MYSELF HALLUCINATED THAT I HAD *EIGHT CHILDREN!*

BUT, APU, YOU *DO* HAVE EIGHT CHILDREN.

NO HECKS REDIT CARDS

AAAAAH!

MEANWHILE...

YES! WORK, MY NOCTURNAL SUPERMAN, **WORK!** WHY I DO BELIEVE I'LL BE ABLE TO LAY OFF HALF OF MY WORKFORCE AT THIS RATE!

YES, WELL DONE, SIR! IF YOU DON'T MIND ME ASKING, WHY AREN'T **YOU** HALLUCINATING LIKE THE REST OF THE TOWN?

I GAVE UP SLEEPING AFTER I WAS VISITED BY THREE GHOSTS ONE CHRISTMAS EVE AND WAS TRICKED INTO BUYING AN EMPLOYEE A GOOSE DINNER!

SLEEPING, BAH HUMBUG!

YOU WERE AHEAD OF YOUR TIME, SIR!

AAAAARGH! READING! IT'S JUST TOO SLOW! I'LL NEVER GET THROUGH ALL OF THESE, EVEN WITH-OUT SLEEP!

THERE MUST BE ANOTHER WAY! A MORE *DIRECT* WAY OF GETTING ALL THIS KNOWLEDGE INSIDE ME.

THAT'S *IT!*

I'LL JUST *EAT* EVERY BOOK IN THE *LIBRARY!*

CHEW!

MUNCH!

RRRRRIP!

MMM... LITERATURE!

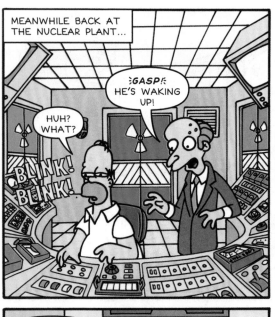

MEANWHILE BACK AT THE NUCLEAR PLANT...

HUH? WHAT?

:GASP!: HE'S WAKING UP!

BLINK! BLINK!

WE NEED ANOTHER '80s TUNE SUNG WITH YOUR DULCET TONES, SMITHERS!

SMITHERS!

SMITHERS!

WHAT AN ODD ECHO. I MUST GET SIMPSON TO FIX THAT!

:GASP!:

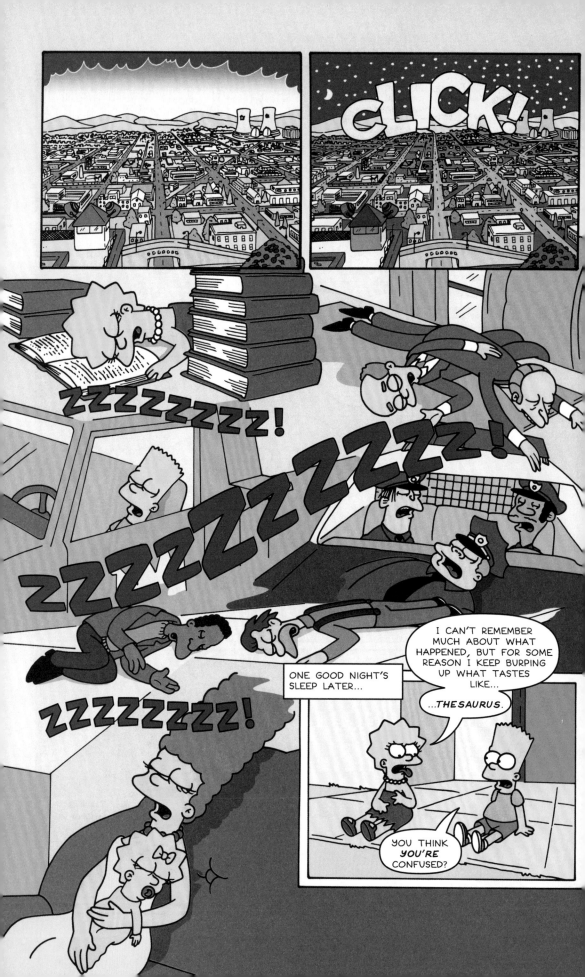

I HAVE NO IDEA WHERE ALL THESE CARS CAME FROM!

BUT I HAVE THE OVERWHELMING URGE TO ENTER MY *INITIALS* SOMEWHERE!

AND AS IT TURNS OUT THE HALLUCINATING TOWNSFOLK WERE VERY OPEN WITH THEIR WALLETS AND WENT ON *SPENDING SPREES* AT LOCAL BUSINESSES. SO, THE ECONOMY SEEMS TO BE *BACK ON TRACK!*

WHY ARE YOU TELLING ME THIS?

I WAS JUST FILLING IN *THE READERS.*

THANKS FOR THE *UPDATE!* WE WERE OUT OF TOWN THE LAST FEW DAYS!

SO EVERYTHING WORKED OUT FOR THE BEST.

OH, YES, ASIDE FROM MY BREAKING EVERY OTHER *BONE IN MY BODY*, IT ALL WENT *RESPLENDENTLY!*

YEAH, THAT'S COOL.

OH, HEY! DO YOU HAVE ANY BACK ISSUES OF *TOMB OF THE WEREWOLF?*

≥SIGH≤ YES. SECOND BOX TO THE LEFT!

MUTANTS

I'M WILLING TO LISTEN TO YOUR *DEMANDS!* JUST LET THE BUNNY GO!

THE FOX HOMER CAUGHT IN THE WOODS DIDN'T WANT TO BE PETTED BY RALPH'S *STICKY FINGERS*, AND, LONG STORY SHORT, HAS TAKEN A RABBIT HOSTAGE.

WHAT'S GOING ON?

HOMER'S DISCOUNT PETTING ZOO $3.00

GRRRRRR!

I'LL GET RALPH TO WEAR GLOVES! AND HOW ABOUT A *CHICKEN?* LET THE RABBIT GO, AND I'LL GIVE YOU A NICE, FAT CHICKEN!

CLUCK!

AAAAH! THE *PECKING!*

CLUCK!

CAAAAAW!

CAAAAAW!

119

MOM, FOR ONCE DAD HAS A POINT. TAKE IT FROM SOMEONE WHO KNOWS, YOU'RE IN A RUT!

LOOK, YOU'VE WORN A PATH IN THE RUG FROM THE BEDROOM TO THE LAUNDRY ROOM...

LAUNDRY ROOM? I THOUGHT THAT WAS A *CLOSET*!

FROM THE *LAUNDRY ROOM* TO THE *KITCHEN*...

AND THE *KITCHEN* TO *MAGGIE'S ROOM* THEN BACK TO YOUR *BEDROOM*! THAT'S THE ROADMAP OF *YOUR LIFE,* MOM.

HRMMM...

THAT NIGHT...

FUNNY STORY. THE THING IS, BEFORE I GOT THE PART ON MEXICAN TELEVISION I DIDN'T A SPEAK A WORD OF SPANISH. I'M ACTUALLY *BELGIAN!*

WHY AREN'T YOU IN BED BY NOW?

I'M TOO *DEPRESSED* TO SLEEP.

WE'LL RETURN TO *A & E'S "BEE-OGRAPHY"* AFTER THESE MESSAGES.

YOU KNOW WHAT MIGHT CHEER YOU UP? MAKING ME A SANDWICH!

IS YOUR LIFE GOING NOWHERE?

YES!

"DO YOU FEEL STUCK IN THE SAME OLD RUT?"

GRRRR! *YES!*

HEY!

"THEN YOU NEED A *LIFE COACH* TO GET YOUR LIFE BACK ON TRACK!"

TIME TO GIVE YOUR SISSY LITTLE LIFE A WORKOUT!

DON'T LET YOUR LIFE PASS YOU BY! *CALL NOW!*

HMMM...

WHAT ARE YOU DOING, MARGE? ORDERING *PIZZA*? BECAUSE, IF SO, I'D LIKE EXTRA CHEESE ON BOTH THE *TOP* AND THE *BOTTOM* OF THE CRUST!

I'M CALLING TO GET A LIFE COACH!

:PFFFT!: THAT'S *STUPID*, MARGE. YOU DON'T NEED ANY-ONE OUTSIDE OF THE HOME TO ENCOURAGE YOU! *I* SUPPORT ANY CHOICES YOU MAKE!

YOU DO *NOT*!

OKAY, NAME *ONE* CHOICE OF YOURS I DIDN'T SUPPORT!

THE CHOICE TO GET A LIFE COACH. YOU JUST SAID IT WAS STUPID!

OH CRAP, SHE'S *RIGHT*! WHAT DO I DO?

I DON'T KNOW. I'M JUST HERE FOR ETHICAL PROBLEMS!

DON'T LOOK AT *ME*! YOU NEVER LISTEN TO WHAT *I* SAY ANYWAY!

...AND THEN THE DEVIL HOMER SAID I SHOULD COME HERE AND DRINK UNTIL I FORGOT WHAT THE ARGUMENT WITH MARGE WAS ABOUT.

YEAH, THEM LITTLE SHOULDER DEVILS GIVE GREAT ADVICE!

MINE TOLD ME TO GET THIS *COOL TATTOO*!

I DIDN'T ⸨GRUNT⸩ REALIZE YOU'D BE *LIVING* HERE.

YEP! I'M YOUR LIFE COACH 24/7! THANKS FOR CARRYING THAT! IT WEIGHS A *TON*, AND WITH MY *SCIATICA*, WELL, DON'T GET ME STARTED...

I GUESS YOU CAN STAY IN BART'S ROOM!

COOOOOOL! KRUSTY THE CLOWN LIVING IN MY ROOM!

I AM YOUR *BIGGEST FAN*, KRUSTY! LOOK, I'VE GOT *ALL YOUR* STUFF!

SORRY, PAL, MY NUMBER ONE FAN IS A KID IN JAPAN!

HE HAS ALL MY PRODUCTS, *AND* HE GOT HIS PARENTS TO TURN THEIR HOME INTO A *KRUSTY SHRINE!*

YOU WANNA BE *NUMBER ONE*? YOU GOTTA TOP *THAT!*

HOMER, CAN I USE YOUR CREDIT CARD TO BUY MORE KRUSTY PRODUCTS ON *EBUY*? IF YOUR ANSWER IS YES, JUST GROAN LIKE YOU'RE HUNGOVER AND WANT ME TO LEAVE YOU ALONE!

⸨GROAN⸩

THANKS!

THE NEXT DAY...

NOW THE **MOST IMPORTANT THING** I CAN TEACH YOU IS MAKING THE MOST OF YOUR LIFE BY EMBRACING YOUR **INNER CLOWN.**

WELL, I DON'T KNOW, I'VE NEVER BEEN THE FUNNIEST MEMBER OF THE FAMILY.

MARGE! WE NEED A NEW **TOILET!**

SEE?

FOR NOW, WE'LL FOCUS ON THESE KEY AREAS OF YOUR LIFE.

LET ME INTRODUCE YOU TO YOUR NEW BEST FRIEND WHO'LL **SPICE UP** ALL THREE!

ROMANCE
HOME-MAKING
PARENTING

SELTZER!

HOMEMAKING...

THIS SELTZER REALLY GETS HOMER'S BEER AND SWEAT STAINS OUT OF THE COUCH!

SPRITZ!

PARENTING...

BART! THOSE COOKIES ARE FOR THE SCHOOL BAKE SALE!

YAAAAH!

SPRITZ!

ROMANCE...

THIS SCENE HAS BEEN CENSORED. TRUST ME, IT'S FOR THE BEST. I'VE SEEN IT, AND I STILL HAVE TROUBLE KEEPING FOOD DOWN.
--EDITOR BILL

THE NEXT DAY...

DING DONG!

AGAIN WITH THE MORNING VISITORS!

OH...HELLO, SOPHIE!

HI, SORRY TO BOTHER YOU. IS MY DAD HERE?

KRUSTY, IT'S FOR YOU!

IF IT'S THE *IRS*, YOU'RE MY *WIFE* AND I'VE ADOPTED *HOMER* AS A *DEDUCTION*!

SOPHIE!

I MEAN, UM... LONG TIME NO SEE! YOU LOOK GOOD!

HOW'S YOUR MOM? STILL A CLOWN-HATING, ARMY VET?

UMM...

LOOK, I KNOW YOU DIDN'T EVEN KNOW I EXISTED UNTIL RECENTLY, BUT MOM'S OFF ON A *TOP SECRET* MILITARY MISSION. SHE SAID YOU'VE GOT TO LOOK AFTER ME WHILE SHE'S *ASSASSINATING* A FOREIGN DICTATOR!

IS IT *MAYOR McCHEESE*? BECAUSE THOSE POOR FRY GUYS HAVE LIVED UNDER HIS BUN OF TYRANNY FOR *TOO LONG*!

HAVE YOU EATEN BREAKFAST YET?

NO, I HAD AN EARLY VIOLIN LESSON THIS MORNING, AND IF I PLAY RACHMANINOFF ON A FULL STOMACH, WELL...THINGS CAN GET PRETTY UGLY.

AND WHAT DID YOU WANT FOR BREAKFAST, KRUSTY?

KRUSTY?

KRUSTY? ARE YOU *HYPER-VENTILATING*?

PANT!

WHEEZE!

:GASP!:

NO, I'M THE UNKNOWN COMIC, AND I THOUGHT THE TIME WAS RIGHT FOR A COMEBACK!

I'M SORRY, I JUST GET SO *NERVOUS* AROUND SOPHIE. I'VE BEEN OUT OF THE PICTURE FOR HER WHOLE LIFE. WHAT COULD WE POSSIBLY *HAVE IN COMMON*?

I CAN'T BELIEVE *YOU'D* BE NERVOUS AROUND A CHILD. YOU ENTERTAIN *MILLIONS* OF THEM EVERY-DAY.

MILLIONS ARE EASY. GETTING THROUGH TO THE *ONE KID THAT MATTERS* ...THAT'S *HARD*!

MAYBE I JUST GOTTA ACCEPT THAT I'M DESTINED TO BE A *DEADBEAT DAD*.

OH, KRUSTY, YOU'LL FIND A WAY TO *CONNECT* WITH SOPHIE. YOU'RE *NOT* A DEADBEAT DAD!

UH...IS MILHOUSE HERE? I WANTED TO BORROW SOME MONEY FROM HIM TO BET ON A COCKFIGHT!

NOW *THAT'S* A DEADBEAT DAD!

LATER...

THIS IS WONDERFUL. A GIRL MY AGE WHO'S *ALSO* A MUSICIAN.

I'M SURE WE'LL BE *BEST FRIENDS*.

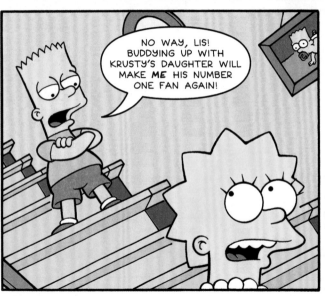

NO WAY, LIS! BUDDYING UP WITH KRUSTY'S DAUGHTER WILL MAKE *ME* HIS NUMBER ONE FAN AGAIN!

YOU CAN'T JUST *USE* HER LIKE THAT!

I CAN'T *NOT* USE HER LIKE THAT!

F.Y.I., WHILE YOU TWO WERE ARGUING, I ATE YOUR BREAK-FASTS!

D'OH!

SHORTLY...

YOU'LL BE SHARING MY ROOM. JUST PUT YOUR STUFF ANYWHERE!

THANKS! I KNOW THIS IS *AWKWARD*. SORRY.

NOT AT ALL. HEY, MAYBE LATER, IF YOU'VE GOT SOME TIME, WE COULD HAVE A *JAM SESSION*!

OH, HI, SOPHIE! *I* WAS WONDERING IF YOU'D LIKE TO HAVE A JAM SESSION, *TOO*!

YOU DON'T PLAY AN INSTRUMENT!

WHAT INSTRUMENT? I MEAN *EAT* JAM!

I'VE GOT APRICOT AND LOGANBERRY!

THAT NIGHT...

C'MON, KRUSTY, YOU CAN *DO* THIS. THINK OF SOMETHING YOU HAVE IN COMMON. SOMETHING *YOUNG* AND *HIP*!

HEY! HEY!

SO, UM...IS IT JUST ME OR HAS "LITTLE HOUSE ON THE PRAIRIE" GOTTEN TOO PREACHY LATELY?

I DON'T KNOW. MOM DOESN'T LIKE ME WATCHING TV. SHE SAYS, "IT CAN LEAD TO DATING CELEBRITIES, AND THEY'RE ALL A BUNCH OF LOWLIFE, BOOZING, FLOPPY SHOE-WEARING DEGENERATES!"

NO OFFENSE.

NONE TAKEN. UM...SO THE BERLIN WALL COMING DOWN. THAT WAS A GOOD THING, HUH?

I WASN'T BORN YET.

RIGHT, RIGHT. SAY, DON'T YOU HATE IT WHEN LARRY HAGMAN SITS IN FRONT OF YOU AT THE EMMY AWARDS AND WON'T TAKE OFF THE COWBOY HAT?

HEY, *STUDY BUDDY*! READY TO CRACK THE BOOKS?

YOU'RE BUSY. I SHOULD GET OUT OF YOUR HAIR!

BUT...

BART, DO YOU HAVE TO PRACTICE YOUR SKATEBOARDING IN HERE? WE'RE TRYING TO DO SCHOOLWORK!

THIS *IS* SCHOOL-WORK, LIS! IT'S ALL ABOUT *PHYSICS*! RIGHT, SOPHIE?

≋SIGH!≋

THE NEXT DAY AT SCHOOL...

GIRL'S WASHROOM

SORRY MY BROTHER'S BEING SUCH A PEST!

OH, HE'S NOT SO BAD. AND YOUR FOLKS ARE GREAT. THEY REALLY SEEM TO *CARE* ABOUT YOU.

AT LEAST BART CAN'T FOLLOW US IN *HERE*.

HI! I'M *BARTINA*, A NEW EXCHANGE STUDENT FROM SHELBYVILLE. SO WHAT ARE WE GIRLS TALKING ABOUT TODAY? MALIBU STACYS? BOYS? *CONTROLLING OUR COOTIES*?

AAAAAARGH!

HEY, GOOD LOOKING! HOW ABOUT A MOVIE SOMETIME?

BART?! WHAT THE...?

HEY, A *FREE MOVIE* IS A *FREE MOVIE*!

POPCORN

131

THE NEXT MORNING...

ξYAAAAWN!ξ

CLICK!

AAAAAAAH!

WHAT DID YOU *DO* TO ME?

YAAAAA!

ξYAWN!ξ

OH, I DYED YOUR HAIR AND APPLIED SOME CLOWN MAKEUP LAST NIGHT. MAN, YOU'RE A *SOUND SLEEPER!*

IT'S ALL PART OF *AWAKENING* YOUR *INNER CLOWN!*

HOW DO I GET THIS *OFF?!!*

OH, IT'S THE *GOOD* STUFF! PARISIAN MIME-STRENGTH. THAT WON'T COME OFF FOR AT LEAST A WEEK!

BUT I HAVE TO DO THE GROCERY SHOPPING!

AN HOUR LATER AT THE GROCERY STORE...

DADDY, LOOK AT THAT FUNNY-LOOKING LADY!

NOW, RALPH, THAT'S RUDE. PEOPLE CAN'T HELP HOW...

OH, I SEE! HA HA! SHE *IS* FUNNY! LAUGH AWAY, RALPH!

HA HA HA!

HEY, CLARABELL. I KNOW WHAT YOU'RE LOOKIN' FOR. COME THIS WAY...

OH, YOU'VE GOT IT ALL WRONG. I'M *MARGE SIMPSON*, AND I DON'T...

STORAGE ROOM

WHOA, SLOW DOWN, KOKO! I DON'T WANT TO HEAR YOUR LIFE STORY. FRANKLY, YOU CLOWNS *DISTURB* AND *FRIGHTEN* ME.

BUT AS LONG AS YOU TAKE THESE *PIES* OFF MY HANDS, YOUR *ALTERNATIVE LIFESTYLE* IS YOUR OWN *TWISTED BUSINESS*!

EXIT

ORANGES 80¢ lb

MONTH-OLD PIES FOR THROWING ONLY

OH MY GOSH! I DIDN'T EVEN *THINK!* I JUST ACTED OUT OF *INSTINCT!*

I'VE NEVER *DONE* ANYTHING LIKE THAT BEFORE!

YOU'VE FINALLY AWAKENED YOUR *INNER CLOWN.* MY JOB HERE IS *DONE!*

WELL...I'LL BE GOING NOW!

KRUSTY?

IS SOMETHING WRONG?

IT'S JUST SPENDING THIS TIME WITH YOU AND SEEING THE GOOD RELATIONSHIP YOU HAVE WITH YOUR KIDS. YOU BOTH MAKE IT LOOK SO EASY!

MAGGIE! IF YOU GET DADDY ONE OF THOSE PIES, I'LL GIVE YOU THIS *CAKE!*

Y'KNOW, IT JUST MAKES ME WISH ME AND SOPHIE WERE *CLOSER.*

DAD, WHY DON'T YOU JUST EAT THE *CAKE?*

:SIGH!: I'VE TRIED EVERYTHING, BUT IT'S USELESS. WE JUST DON'T HAVE ANYTHING IN *COMMON!*

LISA! :MUNCH: GET DADDY A PIE :CHEW: AND I'LL GIVE YOU THIS CAT!

YOU AND SOPHIE HAVE TO STAY FOR AT LEAST ONE MORE DINNER.

WELL... OKAY.

THAT EVENING...

THIS IS A GREAT DINNER, MRS. SIMPSON!

THANK YOU, SOPHIE!

YEAH, I'M REALLY GONNA MISS EATING HERE! WHENEVER MR. TEENY MAKES PASTA. IT'S MORE *MONKEY HAIR* THAN ANGEL HAIR.

EEEEW!

THAT IS *SO* COOL. MOM CAN WE GET A *MONKEY CHEF?*

YOU KNOW WHAT WOULD REALLY HIT THE SPOT FOR DESSERT? *WEEK-OLD PIE!*

HEY, SOPHIE, AFTER DINNER I'D LIKE TO SHOW YOU A SONG I'VE WRITTEN ABOUT US BEING *BEST FRIENDS!*

OH, UM...THAT'S NICE.

SORRY, LISA! SOPHIE IS *MY* BEST FRIEND, AND I'M GONNA PROVE IT IN A PUPPET SHOW I'VE WRITTEN CALLED, "BART AND SOPHIE: SUPER-PALS FOREVER!"

;GASP; ;WHEEZE!;

OH, I GUESS I SHOULD HAVE USED A *CLEAN SOCK* FOR THIS, HUH?

KRUSTY, I'VE BEEN WATCHING YOUR SHOW...

HEY, THAT'S GREAT!

...AND I HOPE YOU DON'T MIND A LITTLE *CONSTRUCTIVE CRITICISM.*

WELL, I...

YOUR SHOW'S AS STALE AS... AS...

WEEK-OLD PIE?

YES! BUT DON'T WORRY! I'VE GOT SOME IDEAS FOR YOUR SHOW THAT YOU'LL *LOVE.*

THERE THEY GO!

YOUR PLAN WORKED. WAY TO GO, MOM!

HOW DID YOU KNOW THAT LISA, HOMER, AND ME ACTING LIKE *SUPER JERKS* WOULD BRING THEM TOGETHER?

WAIT A MINUTE! HOW COME NO ONE TOLD *ME* ABOUT THE ACTING LIKE A JERK PLAN!

YOU DID JUST FINE ON YOUR OWN, HOMEY. YOU SEE, BART, KRUSTY AND SOPHIE JUST NEEDED SOMETHING IN COMMON.

AND NOTHING BRINGS PEOPLE TOGETHER FASTER THAN A *COMMON ENEMY!*

MOM! DAD MADE IT PAST THE BABY GATE!

HE JUMPED OVER?

MORE LIKE *FELL THROUGH!*

JOIN US NEXT MONTH, TRUE BELIEVERS, FOR THE PULSE POUNDING CONCLUSION OF THE FIGHT OF THE CENTURY,

HOMER VS. THE FOX!

WHO WILL GET THE PIE? THE PORTLY PARENT OR THE VICIOUS VULPE?

COME TO THINK OF IT, THAT DOESN'T SOUND GOOD AT ALL. OKAY, FORGET THE WHOLE FOX FIGHT THING. WE'LL COME UP WITH SOMETHING ELSE FOR NEXT ISSUE. IT'LL BE GOOD THOUGH, WE PROMISE. MAYBE WITH MONKEYS. HOMER FIGHTING A MONKEY? PEOPLE LIKE MONKEYS, RIGHT? --BILL